The Perfect Day for a Picnic

Description

Learners explore the phenomenon of weather changing throughout a week (and even throughout a day), beginning with a funny read-aloud about a picnic that unexpectedly gets rained out. They keep track of weather conditions in their area for a week in order to look for patterns. Then, they read a nonfiction book and watch a video about the importance of weather forecasting, especially in severe weather. They apply their understandings by viewing a local weather forecast and discussing how they can prepare for the upcoming weather. Finally, they read a fictional forecast and apply their understandings to decide which day would be the "perfect day for a picnic!"

Alignment With the *Next Generation Science Standards*

Performance Expectations

K-ESS2-1: Use and share observations of local weather conditions to describe patterns over time.

K-ESS3-2: Ask questions to obtain information about the purpose of weather forecasting to prepare for, and respond to, severe weather.

Science and Engineering Practices	Disciplinary Core Ideas	Crosscutting Concepts
Analyzing and Interpreting Data Use observations (firsthand or from media) to describe patterns in the natural and designed world(s) in order to answer scientific questions and solve problems. Using Mathematics and Computational Thinking Use counting and numbers to identify and describe patterns in the natural and designed world(s).	ESS2.D: Weather and Climate Weather is the combination of sunlight, wind, snow or rain, and temperature in a particular region at a particular time. People measure these conditions to describe and record the weather and to notice patterns over time. ESS3.B: Natural Hazards Some kinds of severe weather are more likely than others in a given region. Weather scientists forecast severe weather so that the communities can prepare for and respond to these events.	Patterns Patterns in the natural and human-designed world can be observed, used to describe phenomena, and used as evidence. Scale, Proportion, and Quantity Relative scales allow objects and events to be compared and described (e.g., bigger and smaller, hotter and colder, faster and slower). Stability and Change Some things stay the same while other things change. Things may change slowly or rapidly.

Note: The activities in this lesson will help students move toward the performance expectations listed, which is the goal after multiple activities. However, the activities will not by themselves be sufficient to reach the performance expectations.

Featured Picture Books

TITLE: *Pignic*
AUTHOR: **Matt Phelan**
ILLUSTRATOR: **Matt Phelan**
PUBLISHER: **Greenwillow Books**
YEAR: **2018**
GENRE: **Story**
SUMMARY: *The pigs head out for a "pignic" on a nice, sunny day, but the weather suddenly changes. A storm comes in, but the pigs end up having a great time in the mud left behind from the rain.*

TITLE: ***Weather Near You***
AUTHOR: **Mary Lindeen**
PUBLISHER: **Norwood House Press**
YEAR: **2017**
GENRE: **Narrative Information**
SUMMARY: *This Beginning-to-Read book uses simple text and photographs to describe different types of weather and explain why it is important to check the weather forecast to prepare for the day and be safe.*

Time Needed

This lesson will take several class periods. Suggested scheduling is as follows:

Session 1: Engage with Pignic Read-Aloud

Sessions 1–5: Explore with Keeping Track of Weather

Session 6: Explain with Looking for Patterns, Weather Near You Read-Aloud, and Meet the Helpers Video

Session 7: Elaborate with Local Weather Forecast

Session 8: Evaluate with The Perfect Day for a Picnic

Materials

For Keeping Track of Weather (per class)

- Large outdoor digital thermometer
- Large outdoor alcohol thermometer
- Flag or windsock

Note: Large outdoor digital and alcohol thermometers can be found on Amazon.com or at your local hardware store.

Student Pages

- Keeping Track of Weather
- The Perfect Day for a Picnic
- STEM Everywhere

Background for Teachers

Learning about weather and climate begins in the early grades as simple observations of local weather conditions. Weather is defined as the condition of the atmosphere at a given place and time. Climate is the range of a region's weather over one year or many years. A key understanding about weather is that it varies from day to day (often changing within a day) and seasonally throughout the year, whereas climate is longer term as well as location-sensitive. According to the Framework, students in grades K–2 should be introduced to the idea that when studying weather, people measure weather conditions and record them in an effort to notice patterns over time. In this lesson, students record the weather conditions in their area twice a day for one week and notice simple patterns such as the temperature typically being cooler in the morning than in the afternoon. Another key understanding about weather for grades K–2 is the importance of weather forecasting to help us prepare for and respond to severe weather events. Meteorologists, scientists that study and predict the weather, use a variety of technology to help them predict how the weather will change. Even with current advances in technology, it is impossible to be 100% accurate with the weather forecast. The intricacies of weather are vast and can be difficult to track. However, knowing some basic information about weather can give you an idea of what to expect.

Learning about weather naturally incorporates the crosscutting concept (CCC) of stability and change. Weather is always changing and it can happen quickly or slowly. Most changes in weather occur along fronts, which are the boundaries between two different air masses. A cold front occurs where cold air pushes against warm air. These cold fronts usually quickly move the warm air up and out of the way. The rising air carries water vapor up and, as it rises, it turns into liquid water droplets that clump together and form clouds. The clouds grow big and dark and then it rains, or snows if it is cold enough. Cold fronts typically cause sudden storms that do not last long. After a cold front passes, the sky usually clears and the weather is colder. Warm fronts occur where warm air pushes against cold air. Warm fronts typically move more slowly than cold fronts and therefore change the weather gradually. They cause mild weather, such as a light drizzle. After a warm front passes, the sky usually clears and the weather is warmer. This lesson also incorporates the CCCs of patterns and of scale, proportion, and quantity as students record and compare temperatures and weather conditions and look for patterns in the data. Students use the science and engineering practice (SEP) of analyzing and interpreting data as they make meaning of those patterns, and the SEP of using mathematics and computational thinking as they measure temperature and count the number of days for certain weather conditions.

Learning Progressions

Below are the DCI grade band endpoints for grades K–2 and 3–5. These are provided to show how student understanding of the DCIs in this lesson will progress in future grade levels.

DCIs	Grades K–2	Grades 3–5
ESS2.D: Weather and Climate	• Weather is the combination of sunlight, wind, snow or rain, and temperature in a particular region at a particular time. People measure these conditions to describe and record the weather and to notice patterns over time.	• Scientists record patterns of the weather across different times and areas so that they can make predictions about what kind of weather might happen next. • Climate describes a range of an area's typical weather conditions and the extent to which those conditions vary over the years.
ESS3.B: Natural Hazards	• Some kinds of severe weather are more likely than others in a given region. Weather scientists forecast severe weather so that the communities can prepare for and respond to these events.	• A variety of natural hazards result from natural processes. Humans cannot eliminate natural hazards but can take steps to reduce their impacts.

Source: Willard, T., ed. 2015. The NSTA quick-reference guide to the NGSS: Elementary school. Arlington, VA: NSTA Press.

engage

Pignic Read-Aloud

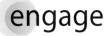

Connecting to the Common Core
Reading: Literature
CRAFT AND STRUCTURE: K.6

Inferring

Show students the cover of Pignic and ask them what they think the title means. (Using the cover illustration, they should be able to infer that a "pignic" is a picnic for pigs.) Point to Matt Phelan's name on the cover and explain that he is both the author and illustrator of this book. He tells the story in words and pictures. Read the first two-page spread that says, "It's a perfect day for a pignic." Spend some time noticing the details in the illustration. Ask

? Have you ever had a picnic outside? What was it like? (Answers will vary.)

? What is the perfect day for a picnic? (a sunny, warm day)

? How does the illustrator show that in the picture? (blue sky, few clouds, birds flying, green grass)

? What do you think he used to make this picture? (Answers will vary. Explain that the illustrator used watercolor paints and colored pencil to create the illustrations.)

? How many pigs are in the illustration? (7)

? What else do you notice about the illustration? (Students may notice the wolf on the left-hand side of the page and the turtle on the right-hand side.)

Tell students that you will read the words, but you would like them to pay close attention to the illustrations because they will tell more of the story than just the words. As you read the book aloud, ask

? What is happening in this picture?

? What do you think will happen next?

? How do the pigs feel in this picture? How can you tell?

? Were you surprised that happened?

Making Connections: Text to Self

After reading the book, ask

? Have you ever been outside and the weather changed suddenly? Where were you and what did you do? (Answers will vary.)

explore

Keeping Track of Weather

Tell students that they are going to be keeping track of the weather conditions in the morning and afternoon each day for a whole week of school in order to look for patterns in the weather. Ask

? What information should we record about the weather? (the temperature, and whether it is rainy, snowy, foggy, sunny, cloudy, or windy)

Give each student a copy of the Keeping Track of Weather student page and project it on the board if possible. Have students look at the first column (Monday). Ask

? How will we find out if it is sunny or cloudy? (Look outside.)

? How will we find out if it is rainy, snowy, or foggy? (Look outside.)

? How will we find out if it is windy? (Look at trees or the flag. Note: If you do not have trees or a flag visible outside your window, you could put up a small flag or windsock.)

? How will we find out what the temperature is outside? (Use a thermometer.)

Connecting to the Common Core
Mathematics
MEASUREMENT AND DATA: K.MD.A1, K.MD.A2

> **SEP: Using Mathematics and Computational Thinking**
> Use counting and numbers to identify and describe patterns in the natural and designed world(s).

Show students a large outdoor alcohol thermometer and a large outdoor digital thermometer. Explain that these are two different kinds of thermometers, but they are both used for measuring temperature. Hold up the alcohol thermometer and point out the glass tube. Tell students that as the temperature gets hotter, the red liquid inside the tube moves up. They can find the temperature by reading the number at the top of the red line. Show them the digital thermometer. Explain that this thermometer shows the temperature on the screen. Tell students that there are two scales commonly used for measuring air temperature—Celsius and Fahrenheit. (Fahrenheit is used for this lesson because air temperature is almost always reported in degrees Fahrenheit in U.S. weather forecasts.) Demonstrate how to read the temperature on each thermometer.

Show students the suction cups that are used to hang the thermometers on a flat surface. Ask

? Where do you think we should place these thermometers to be able to see the temperature outside from the inside of our classroom? Why? (outside our classroom window or a window

nearby the classroom so that we can read them easily from inside the classroom)

Read the instructions that come with the thermometers for information on how and where to hang your thermometers.

Use the readings on the thermometers to fill out the Monday column together, recording the temperature and circling all the weather conditions that apply. Repeat this procedure every morning and afternoon for the rest of the week. As you fill out the chart together over the week, ask comparative questions, such as

? Was the temperature higher in the morning or afternoon today?

? What is the temperature difference between the morning and afternoon today?

? How does the temperature this morning compare to the temperature yesterday morning?

? How does today's weather compare to yesterday's?

? How is the weather this afternoon different from the weather this morning?

> **SEP: Analyzing and Interpreting Data**
> Use observations (firsthand or from media) to describe patterns in the natural world in order to answer scientific questions.

explain

Looking for Patterns

After students have filled out their Keeping Track of Weather pages, invite them to make some observations and look for patterns in their weather data. First, prompt some general observations by asking questions, such as

? How many days was it sunny?

? How many days did it rain?

? Which was more common this week, sunny or rainy days?

> **CCC: Patterns**
> Patterns in the natural and human-designed world can be observed and used as evidence.

> **CCC: Scale, Proportion, and Quantity**
> Relative scales allow objects and events to be compared and described (e.g., bigger and smaller, hotter and colder, faster and slower).

Explain that a pattern is a repeated or regular way that something happens. Ask

LOOKING FOR PATTERNS

? Do you see any patterns in your weather data? (Answers will vary, but students may notice things like it is foggy in the mornings but not in the afternoons, or if it is rainy it is also cloudy.)

? Do you notice a pattern in the temperature in the morning compared to the afternoon? (Depending on your weather that week, students may notice that the temperature in the morning is typically cooler than the temperature in the afternoon.)

Ask

? How did the weather affect you during that week?

? Did you have to dress a certain way?

? Were any of your activities canceled?

? Did you play outside or inside?

? How can you find out what the weather will be before you leave your house? (watch the news, check a weather app, etc.)

Connecting to the Common Core
Reading: Informational Text
KEY IDEAS AND DETAILS: K.1

Weather Near You Read-Aloud

 Determining Importance

Show students the cover of Weather Near You and tell them that as you read, you would like them to listen for the reasons that it is important to check the weather forecast regularly.

 Questioning

Read the book aloud, then ask

? Why is it important to check the weather forecast regularly? (so you can wear the right clothes, plan activities, bring an umbrella or sunglasses, be safe, etc.)

? Why is it not enough just to look out the window and see what the weather looks like before you leave? (because weather can change throughout the day)

Explain that weather is always changing. Sometimes it changes quickly, like in the Pignic book, and sometimes it changes more slowly.

CCC: Stability and Change
Some things stay the same while other things change.

Things may change slowly or rapidly.

Rereading

Reread pages 20–27 about how the weather can change. Explain that even though you might look out the window in the morning and it is sunny, rain could come later in the day. So it might be necessary to bring along a rain jacket or umbrella. Revisit the Keeping Track of Weather student page and point out any days where the weather changed from morning to afternoon. Ask

? Have you ever watched a weather forecast on the news? (Answers will vary.)

Meet the Helpers Video

Explain that a person trained in forecasting the weather is called a meteorologist. Tell students that you have a video that can help them learn more about how a meteorologist uses science and technology to keep us safe and prepared for weather changes. Show the 2:27-minute video titled "In-Depth: Meteorologist" from the Meet the Helpers website (see "Websites" section).

After the video, ask

? How do meteorologists keep us safe? (They tell us what the weather will be so we can wear the right clothes and prepare for severe weather.)

? What kinds of severe weather do we have in our area? (Answers will depend on where you live, but could include thunderstorms, hurricanes, blizzards, tornadoes, or dust storms.)

? What do we do to prepare for these kinds of severe weather? (Students may have had experiences with severe weather. Allow them to share their experiences. Assure students that meteorologists, teachers, and parents are all helpers who know what to do to keep them safe in weather emergencies.)

Explain that forecasting the weather is not always exact. Meteorologists use all kinds of weather measurements to forecast what the weather will be. They study weather patterns and have good predictions of what will come next. Meteorologists can sometimes be wrong because weather can change quickly. But most of the time, they can give us a pretty accurate idea of what is to come.

elaborate

Local Weather Forecast

Find a recording of a current weather forecast from one of your local news stations' websites. The first time you watch it together, ask students to listen for what the weather forecast is for the next day. Then ask

? How should we dress for tomorrow? Why?

? Do you think we will have indoor or outdoor recess? Why?

? Will the weather in the morning be the same as in the afternoon?

> **SEP: Analyzing and Interpreting Data**
> Use observations (firsthand or from media) to describe patterns in the natural world in order to answer scientific questions.

Then watch the same forecast again, but this time ask students to watch and listen for the tools that meteorologists use to show us the forecast. Watch and then ask

? What tools did the meteorologist use to help us understand the forecast? (maps, different colors, numbers, pictures of things like the Sun, clouds, and rain)

You can also point out that meteorologists use a lot of technology to forecast and share the weather, such as radar, computers, microphones, and television cameras.

You may also want to show students a weather app, such as The Weather Channel, Weather Bug, or Hello Weather so they can see the different ways that the forecast can be shared.

evaluate

The Perfect Day for a Picnic

Connecting to the Common Core
Writing
RESEARCH TO BUILD AND PRESENT KNOWLEDGE: K.8

Writing

Give each student a copy of The Perfect Day for a Picnic student pages. Read the directions aloud, "Look at the weather forecast. What do you think would be the perfect day to have a picnic? Circle it." Discuss the weather forecast for each day on the chart. Have students circle the day when they would plan their picnic.

After students circle the day they chose, read the next question aloud, "Why did you choose that day?" and have them write their answers.

Finally, read the third prompt aloud, "Draw yourself dressed for a picnic on that day." Ask students to think about what they would wear in their picture and what they would need to bring. Encourage them to include those details and label them if possible.

Although Thursday's weather (75°F with warm sunshine) might seem the best day for a picnic, students may choose any day of the week as long as they can give evidence and explain their reasoning for why that would be the "perfect" day.

THE PERFECT DAY FOR A PICNIC

> **SEP: Analyzing and Interpreting Data**
> Use observations (firsthand or from media) to describe patterns in the natural world in order to answer scientific questions.

> **CCC: Patterns**
> Patterns in the natural and human-designed world can be observed and used as evidence.

STEM Everywhere

Give students the STEM Everywhere student page as a way to involve their families and extend their learning. They can do the activity with an adult helper and share their results with the class. If students do not have access to these materials at home, you may choose to have them complete this activity at school.

Opportunities for Differentiated Instruction

This box lists questions and challenges related to the lesson that students may select to research, investigate, or innovate. Students may also use the questions as examples to help them generate their own questions. These questions can help you move your students from the teacher-directed investigation to engaging in the science and engineering practices in a more student-directed format.

Extra Support

For students who are struggling to meet the lesson objectives, provide a question and guide them in the process of collecting research or helping them design procedures or solutions.

Extensions

For students with high interest or who have already met the lesson objectives, have them choose a question (or pose their own question), conduct their own research, and design their own procedures or solutions.

After selecting one of the questions in this box or formulating their own questions, students can individually or collaboratively make predictions, design investigations or surveys to test their predictions, collect evidence, devise explanations, design solutions, or examine related resources. They can communicate their findings through a science notebook, at a poster session or gallery walk, or by producing a media project.

Research

Have students brainstorm researchable questions:

? What are the different types of clouds?

? What is lightning?

? What was the hottest day on record for our location? What was the coldest day on record for our location?

Investigate

Have students brainstorm testable questions to be solved through science or math:

? What is the difference between the highest temperature reading this week and the lowest temperature reading this week?

? Can you use a rain gauge to measure rainfall?

? How many days did it rain in the past month?

Innovate

Have students brainstorm problems to be solved through engineering:

? Can you design a test to see if different fabrics are waterproof?

? Can you design a way to improve an umbrella?

? Can you design a windsock?

Website

 Meet the Helpers: "In-Depth: Meteorologist" Video
www.meetthehelpers.org/the-helpers

More Books to Read

Boothroyd, J. 2014. *What is severe weather?* Minneapolis, MN: LernerClassroom.
Summary: Simple text and illustrations introduce different types of severe weather—from thunderstorms to blizzards—and provide information on how to stay safe in each kind of severe weather.

Branley, F. M. 2000. *Snow is falling*. New York: HarperCollins.
Summary: This Let's-Read-and-Find-Out Science Stage 1 book explains why snow is good for plants, animals, and people, and how it can be dangerous too.

Sayre, A. P. 2015. *Raindrops roll*. New York: Simon & Schuster.
Summary: This beautifully photo-illustrated nonfiction picture book shares the wonders of rain and the water cycle.

Sayre, A. P. 2016. *Best in snow*. New York: Simon & Schuster.
Summary: This beautifully photo-illustrated nonfiction picture book celebrates the beauty of snowfall.

Sherman, J. 2003. *Gusts and gales: A book about wind*. Minneapolis, MN: Picture Window Books.
Summary: Learn how wind helps your kite fly, blows the leaves from trees, and can turn into a hurricane or tornado.

Sherman, J. 2003. *Nature's fireworks: A book about lightning*. Minneapolis, MN: Picture Window Books.
Summary: Learn what makes lightning flash across the sky. End matter includes safety tips on how to stay safe when there is lightning.

Sherman, J. 2003. *Shapes in the sky: A book about clouds*. Minneapolis, MN: Picture Window Books.
Summary: Learn what clouds are made of and the different types of clouds.

Sherman, J. 2003. *Splish! Splash! A book about rain*. Minneapolis, MN: Picture Window Books.
Summary: Find out why rain is so important, and what happens when it rains too much and when it rains too little.

Name: _____

Keeping Track of Weather

	Monday	Tuesday	Wednesday	Thursday	Friday
MORNING	Temperature ___ Sunny, Cloudy, Windy, Rainy, Snowy, Foggy	Temperature ___ Sunny, Cloudy, Windy, Rainy, Snowy, Foggy	Temperature ___ Sunny, Cloudy, Windy, Rainy, Snowy, Foggy	Temperature ___ Sunny, Cloudy, Windy, Rainy, Snowy, Foggy	Temperature ___ Sunny, Cloudy, Windy, Rainy, Snowy, Foggy
AFTERNOON	Temperature ___ Sunny, Cloudy, Windy, Rainy, Snowy, Foggy	Temperature ___ Sunny, Cloudy, Windy, Rainy, Snowy, Foggy	Temperature ___ Sunny, Cloudy, Windy, Rainy, Snowy, Foggy	Temperature ___ Sunny, Cloudy, Windy, Rainy, Snowy, Foggy	Temperature ___ Sunny, Cloudy, Windy, Rainy, Snowy, Foggy

National Science Teaching Association

Name: _____

The Perfect Day for a Picnic

(Page 1)

1. Look at the weather forecast. What do you think would be the perfect day to have a picnic? Circle it.

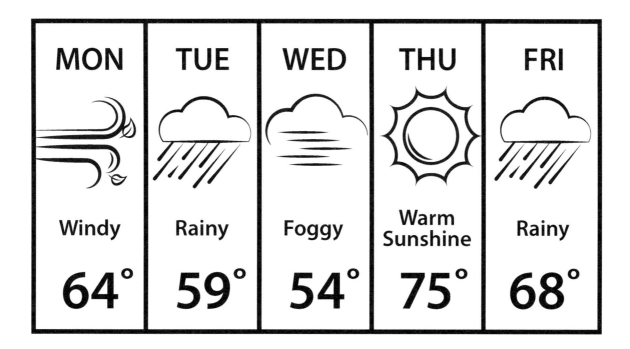

MON	TUE	WED	THU	FRI
Windy	Rainy	Foggy	Warm Sunshine	Rainy
64°	59°	54°	75°	68°

2. The perfect day for a picnic would be _____

because _____

_____

_____

Name: _____

The Perfect Day for a Picnic

(Page 2)

3. Draw yourself dressed for the picnic.

National Science Teaching Association

STEM Everywhere

Dear Families,

At school, we have been learning about **how weather affects our lives.** It is important to check the weather forecast so we know what to wear and how to stay safe. To find out more, ask your learner the following questions and discuss their answers:

- What did you learn?
- What was your favorite part of the lesson?
- What are you still wondering?

At home, you can check the weather forecast together using an app, website, newspaper, or by watching a weather forecast on the news. Write the name of the source you used to check the weather.

We used _____ to find out

what the weather will be tomorrow.

Tomorrow's weather will be _____ .

Help your learner draw and label a picture of your family prepared for tomorrow's weather.